𝔊. 𝔖chirmer's 𝔈ditions
of
𝔒ratorios and 𝔔antatas

Judas Maccabæus

An Oratorio

The Music by

G. F. HÄNDEL

Words by the
REV. THOS. MORELL, D. D.

A Special Concert Edition by
FRANK VAN DER STUCKEN

Ed. 709

G. SCHIRMER

New York / London

JUDAS MACCABÆUS

CHARACTERS REPRESENTED

JUDAS MACCABÆUS }
ISRAELITISH MAN } *Tenor*
ISRAELITISH WOMAN, *Soprano*

SIMON, THE HIGH PRIEST }
ISRAELITISH MESSENGER } *Bass*

ISRAELITISH WOMAN }
A PRIEST } *Alto*

CHORUS: THE PEOPLE OF ISRAEL

ARGUMENT

PART I.—Lamentations for the death of Mattathias (the father of Judas Maccabæus and Simon), by whom the Jewish people had been roused to resist the cruelties and oppressions of Antiochus Epiphanes, the Syrian king, in his attempt to suppress their religion and liberties.—The divine favour invoked.—Judas recognized as leader.—Appeal to the patriotism of the people, and their response.—The value of liberty.—Preparations for war.—Pious trust in God, and heroic resolve to conquer or die.

PART II.—Celebration of the victories gained over the armies of Apollonius, the Governor of Samaria, and Seron, the Deputy Governor of Cœlesyria ; and the valour of Judas.—Renewal of war by a division of the Syrian army from Egypt, under Gorgias, and the despondency it occasions amongst the Israelites.—Judas again arouses the failing courage of the people, and they set out to meet the enemy.—Those who remain behind utter their detestation of the Heathen Idolatries, by which the Sanctuary at Jerusalem had been desecrated, and their determination to worship only the God of Israel.

PART III.—Feast of the Dedication at Jerusalem, after Judas and his followers had recovered and restored the Sanctuary, and re-established the liberties of his country.—Return of Judas from his final victory over Nicanor and his confederates.

Part the First

No. 1. OVERTURE.

SCENE.—*Modin.*

ISRAELITES, *Men and Women, lamenting the death of* MATTATHIAS, *Father of* JUDAS MACCABÆUS.

No. 2. CHORUS.

Mourn, ye afflicted children, the remains
Of captive Judah, mourn in solemn strains,
Your sanguine hopes of liberty give o'er ;
Your hero, friend, and father is no more.

No. 3. DUET.

Israelitish Man (Tenor) and *Woman* (Soprano).

From this dread scene, these adverse pow'rs,
Ah ! whither shall we fly ?
O Solyma, thy boasted tow'rs
In smoky ruins lie !

No. 4. CHORUS.

For Sion lamentation make
With words that weep, and tears that speak.

No. 5. RECIT.—*Simon* (Bass).

Not vain is all this storm of grief ;
To vent our sorrows, gives relief.

Wretched indeed! But let not Judah's race
Their ruin with desponding arms embrace.

No. 6. AIR.—*Simon.*

Pious orgies, pious airs,
Decent sorrow, decent pray'rs,
Will to the Lord ascend, and move
His pity, and regain His love.

No. 7. CHORUS.

O Father, whose Almighty pow'r
The heav'ns, and earth, and seas adore,
The hearts of Judah, Thy delight,
In one defensive band unite,
And grant a leader bold and brave,
If not to conquer, born to save.

No. 8. RECIT.—*Simon* (Bass).

I feel the Deity within,
Who, the bright Cherubim between,
    His radiant glory erst display'd;
To Israel's distressful pray'r
He hath vouchsaf'd a gracious ear,
    And points out Maccabæus to their aid:
Judas shall set the captive free,
And lead us on to victory.

No. 9. AIR.

Arm, arm, ye brave! a noble cause,
    The cause of Heav'n, your zeal demands;
In defence of your nation, religion, and laws,
    The almighty Jehovah will strength-en your hands.

CHORUS.

We come, we come, in bright array,
Judah, thy sceptre to obey!

No. 10. RECIT.—*Judas* (Tenor).

'Tis well, my friends! With trans-port I behold
The spirit of our fathers, famed of old

For their exploits in war.—Oh, may their fire
With active courage you, their sons, inspire!
    As, when the mighty Joshua fought,
    And those amazing wonders wrought,
Stood still, obedient to his voice, the sun,
Till kings he had destroy'd, and kingdoms won.

No. 11. AIR.—*Judas.*

Call forth thy pow'rs, my soul, and dare
The conflict of unequal war:
Great is the glory of the conqu'ring sword
That triumphs in sweet liberty re-stor'd.

CHORUS.

Lead on, lead on! Judah disdains
The galling load of hostile chains!

No. 12. RECIT.

Israelitish Woman (Soprano).

To Heav'n's almighty King we kneel,
For blessings on this exemplary zeal.
Bless him, Jehovah, bless him, and once more
To Thy own Israel liberty restore.

No. 13. AIR.

Israelitish Woman.

O Liberty, thou choicest treasure,
Seat of virtue, source of pleasure!
Life, without thee, knows no blessing,
No endearment worth caressing.

DUET (Soprano and Alto)

Come, ever-smiling liberty,
    And with thee bring thy jocund train;
For thee we pant, and sigh for thee,
    With whom eternal pleasures reign!

No. 14.   RECIT.—*Judas* (Tenor).

My zealous father, now at rest
In the eternal mansions of the blest:
"Can ye behold," said he, "the
   miseries
In which ere long insulted Judah lies?
Can ye behold their dire distress,
And not, at least, attempt redress?"
Then faintly, with expiring breath:
"Resolve, my sons, on liberty, or,
   death."

We come! O see, thy sons prepare
The rough habiliments of war,
With hearts intrepid, and revengeful
   hands,
To execute, O Sire, thy dread com-
   mands.

No. 15.   TRIO AND CHORUS.

Disdainful of danger, we'll rush on
   the foe,
That Thy pow'r, O Jehovah, all
   nations may know.

No. 16.   RECIT.—*Simon* (Bass).

Haste ye, my brethren, haste ye to
   the field.
Dependent on the Lord, our strength
   and shield.

No. 17.   CHORUS.

Hear us, O Lord, on Thee we call,
Resolv'd on conquest, or a glorious
   fall!

———

Part the Second.

SCENE.—*The same.*

The ISRAELITES *celebrating the return
of* JUDAS *from the victories over*
APOLLONIUS *and* SERON.

No. 18.   CHORUS.

Fall'n is the foe: so fall Thy foes, O
   Lord,
Where warlike Judas wields his right-
   eous sword.

**No. 19.   DUET (Soprano and
Tenor) AND CHORUS.**

Sion now her head shall raise,
Tune your harps to songs of praise.

No. 20.   RECIT.
Israelitish Woman (Soprano).

Oh, let eternal honours crown his
   name,
Judas, first Worthy in the rolls of
   fame.
Say, "He put on the breast-plate as
   a giant,
And girt his warlike harness about
   him.
In his acts he was like a lion,
And like a lion's whelp roaring for
   his prey."

No. 21.   AIR.—(*Israelitish Woman*).

From mighty kings he took the spoil,
And with his acts made Judah smile.

**No. 22.   DUET (OR CHILDREN'S
CHOIR) AND CHORUS.**

Hail, Judea, happy land!
Salvation prospers in his hand.

No. 23.   RECIT.—*Judas* (Tenor).

Thanks to my brethren: but, look
   up to Heav'n!
To Heav'n let all glory and all praise
   be giv'n;
To Heav'n give your applause, nor
   add the second cause,
As once your fathers did in Midian,
Saying, "The sword of God and
   Gideon."
It was the Lord that for his Israel
   fought,
And this our wonderful salvation
   wrought.

No. 24.   AIR.—*Judas.*

How vain is man, who boasts in fight
The valour of gigantic might,
And dreams not that a hand unseen
Directs and guides this weak machine.

No. 25. RECIT.

Israelitish Messenger (Bass).

O Judas, O my brethren!
New scenes of bloody war
In all their horrors rise.
Prepare, prepare,
Or soon we fall a sacrifice
To great Antiochus: From th'
Egyptian coast
(Where Ptolemy hath Memphis and
Pelusium lost)
He sends the valiant Gorgias, and
commands
His proud victorious bands
To root out Israel's strength, and to
erase
Ev'ry memorial of the sacred place.

No. 26. AIR AND CHORUS.

Ah! wretched, wretched Israel! fall'n
how low,
From joyous transport to desponding woe.

No. 27. RECIT.—*Judas* (Tenor).

My arms! against this Gorgias will
I go!
The Idumean governor shall know
How vain, how ineffective his design,
While rage his leader, and Jehovah
mine.

No. 28. AIR AND CHORUS.

Sound an alarm, your silver trumpets
sound,
And call the brave, and only brave,
around!
Who listeth, follow: - to the field
again!
Justice, with courage, is a thousand
men.

CHORUS.

We hear, we hear the pleasing, dread-
ful call,
And follow thee to conquest:—If to
fall,
For laws, religion, liberty, we fall.

No. 29. RECIT.—*Simon* (Bass).

Enough! to Heav'n we leave the
rest,
Such gen'rous ardour firing ev'ry
breast,
We may divide our cares. The field
be thine,
O Judas, and the Sanctuary mine.
For Sion, holy Sion, seat of God,
In ruinous heaps is by the heathen
trod.
Down, down with the polluted altars,
down!
Hurl Jupiter Olympius from his
throne,
Nor reverence Bacchus with his ivy
crown!
Our fathers never knew him, or his
hated crew,
Or, knowing, scorn'd such idol
vanities.

No. 30. CHORUS.

We never, never will bow down
To the rude stock, or sculptur'd stone:
We worship God, and God alone.

———

Part the Third.

Mount Sion.

ISRAELITISH PRIESTS, ETC., *having
recovered the Sanctuary.*

No. 31. AIR.—*Priest* (Alto).

Father of Heav'n, from Thy eternal
throne
Look with an eye of blessing down,
While we prepare, with holy rites,
To solemnize the Feast of Lights.
And thus our grateful hearts employ,
And in Thy praise
This altar raise
With carols of triumphant joy.

No. 32. RECIT.

Israelitish Woman (Soprano).

O grant it, Heav'n, that our long
    woes may cease,
And Judah's daughters taste the
    calm of peace;
Sons, brothers, husbands, to bewail
    no more,
Tortur'd at home, or havock'd in
    the war.

No. 33. AIR.—*Israelitish Woman.*

So shall the lute and harp awake,
    And sprightly voice sweet descant
    run,
Seraphic melody to make,
    In the pure strains of Jesse's son.

No. 34. RECIT.

Israelitish Messenger (Bass).

From Capharsalama on eagle wings I
    fly,
With tidings of impetuous joy:
Came Lysias, with his host array'd
In coat of mail; their massy shields
Of gold and brass flash'd lightning
    o'er the fields;
But Judas, undismay'd,
Met, fought, and vanquish'd all the
    rageful train.
But lo! the conqueror comes; and
    on his spear,
To dissipate all fear,
He bears the vaunter's head and hand,
That threaten'd desolation to the land.

———

Near Jerusalem.

ISRAELITISH YOUTHS AND MAIDENS
meeting JUDAS *on his return from
the victory over* NICANOR.

No. 35. CHORUS.
(With Children's Choir.)

See, the conqu'ring hero comes!
Sound the trumpets, beat the drums;
Sports prepare, the laurel bring,
Songs of triumph to him sing.

See the godlike youth advance,
Breathe the flutes, and lead the dance;
Myrtle-wreaths and roses twine,
To deck the hero's brow divine.

No. 36. MARCH.

No. 37. CHORUS.

Sing unto God, and high affections
    raise
To crown this conquest with un-
    measur'd praise.

No. 38. RECIT.—*Judas* (Tenor).

Sweet flow the strains, that strike my
    feasted ear;
Angels might stoop from Heav'n to
    hear
The comely songs ye sing
To Israel's Lord and King.

No. 39. AIR.—*Judas.*

No unhallow'd desire
Our breasts shall inspire,
Nor lust of unbounded pow'r:
    But peace to obtain,
    Free peace let us gain,
And conquest shall ask no more.

No. 40. DUET.
(Soprano and Alto.)

O lovely peace, with plenty crown'd,
Come, spread thy blessings all around;
Let fleecy flocks the hills adorn,
And valleys smile with wavy corn.
Let the shrill trumpet cease, nor
    other sound
But nature's songsters wake the
    cheerful morn.

No. 41. AIR (*Simon*) AND CHORUS.
(With Children's Choir.)

Rejoice, O Judah, and in songs
    divine,
With cherubim and seraphim har-
    monious join.
Hallelujah! Amen!

INDEX

Part the First

JUDAS MACCABAEUS

Part I

Rev. Thos. Morell, D.D.

A special Concert Edition
by Frank van der Stucken

№ 1. OVERTURE

20750cx

№ 2. CHORUS.—"Mourn, ye afflicted children"

he - ro is no more, your fa-ther is no more, your fa-ther

he - ro is no more, your fa-ther is no more, your fa-ther

more, your fa-ther is no more, mourn, your fa-ther

more, your fa-ther is no more, mourn, your fa-ther

is no more, mourn, your fa-ther is no more.

is no more, mourn, your fa-ther is no more.

is no more, mourn, your fa-ther is no more.

is no more, mourn, your fa-ther is no more.

№ 3. DUET.—"From this dread scene"

ISRAELITISH WOMAN *(Soprano)*

fly from this dread scene? O So-ly-ma,

- - - - - y ru - ins lie!

B

thy boast-ed tow'rs in smok - - - y

From this dread scene, these ad - verse pow'rs,

B

ru - ins lie! O

Ah! whith-er shall we fly? ah! whith-er shall we fly? O So - ly-ma!

15

20750

p
So-ly-ma, thy boast-ed tow'rs In smok-y ru-ins
mp
p
O So-ly-ma, thy boast-ed tow'rs
p
lie, thy boast-ed tow'rs in smok - - -
In smok-y ru-ins lie, in smok - - - -
poco rit.
a tempo
- - - y ru-ins lie! O So-ly-ma,
mf
- - - y ru-ins lie! From this dread
poco rit.
p
a tempo mp
mf
thy boast-ed tow'rs In smoky ru-ins lie, in smok - - -
scene, these ad - verse pow'rs, Ah! whith-er shall we

№ 4. CHORUS._"For Sion lamentation make"

Larghetto

18

20750

№ 5. RECIT. – "Not vain is all this storm of grief"

SIMON (Bass)

Not vain is all this storm of grief; To vent our

sor - rows, gives re - lief. Wretch - ed in - deed! But

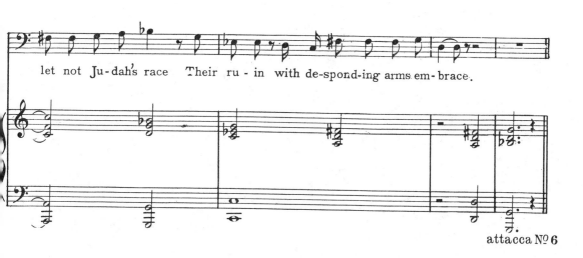

let not Ju - dah's race Their ru - in with de - spond-ing arms em - brace.

attacca № 6

Nº 6. AIR.—"Pious orgies, pious airs"

Largo e sostenuto

SIMON

Pi-ous or-gies, pi-ous airs, De-cent sor-row,

de-cent pray'rs, Will to the Lord as-cend, and

move His pit-y, His pit-y, and re-gain His love.

Pi-ous or-gies, pi-ous airs, De-cent sor-row, de-cent

sor-row, de - cent pray'rs, Will to the

Lord as-cend, and move His pit-y, His pit-y, and re-gain His

24

love. Pi - ous or - gies,   pi - ous airs, De - cent

sor - row, de - cent pray'rs,   Will to the Lord as - cend, and

move His pit - y, His pit - y, and re - gain His

love.

Nº 7. CHORUS.—"O Father, whose almighty pow'r"

26

seas a - dore, The

seas a - dore, The

seas a - dore, The

seas a - dore, The

hearts of Ju - dah, Thy de - light, In one de - fen - sive

hearts of Ju - dah, Thy de - light, In one de - fen - sive

hearts of Ju - dah, Thy de - light, In one de - fen - sive

hearts of Ju - dah, Thy de - light, In one de - fen - sive

band u - nite,

band u - nite,

band u - nite,

band u - nite,

20750

30

20750

№ 8. RECIT.—"I feel the Deity within"

Is - ra - el's dis - tress - ful pray'r He hath vouch-saf'd a gra - cious

ear, And points out Macca - bæ - us to their aid: Ju-das shall set the cap-tive

free, And lead us on to vic - to - ry.

attacca № 9

N⁰ 9. AIR AND CHORUS.—Arm, arm, ye brave!"

no - ble cause, the cause of Heav'n, your zeal de-mands.

A

Arm, arm, ye brave! arm, arm, ye brave! a no - ble cause!

Arm, arm, arm, arm, ye brave! Arm, arm, arm, arm, ye brave! A

no - ble cause, the cause of Heav'n, your zeal demands, your zeal demands; Arm, arm ye brave! A

no - ble cause, the cause of Heav'n, your zeal demands, your zeal, the

36

20750

40

20750

JUDAS MACCABÆUS (Tenor)

'Tis well, my friends! With trans-port I be-hold The spir-it of our fa-thers, fam'd of old For their ex-ploits in war. Oh, may their fire With ac-tive cou-rage you, their sons, in - spire! As, when the might-y Josh-ua fought, And those a-maz-ing won-ders wrought, Stood still, o-be-dient to his voice, the sun, Till kings he had de-stroy'd, and king-doms won.

Nº 11. AIR AND CHORUS._"Call forth thy pow'rs, my soul"

Call forth thy pow'rs, my soul, and dare!

Call forth thy pow'rs, my soul, and dare The con-flict, the

con-flict of un - e - - - qual war,

cresc. and dare the

conflict of un - e - qual

attacca Chorus

CHORUS.__"Lead on, lead on!"

48

20750

Nº 12. RECIT._"To Heav'n's almighty King we kneel"

ISRAELITISH WOMAN (*Soprano*)

To Heav'n's al-might-y King we kneel, For

bless-ings on this ex-em-pla-ry zeal. Bless him, Je-ho-vah, bless him,

and once more To Thy own Is-ra-el lib-er-ty re-store.

attacca Nº 1

№ 13. AIR AND DUET

"O liberty, thou choicest treasure"

dearment worth ca-ress - ing; Seat of vir-tue, source of pleasure!

O _____ lib-er -ty, thou choic-est treas-ure, Seat of vir-tue, source of

pleasure! Life, without thee, knows no bless-ing, Life, without thee, knows no blessing, No en-

dear-ment, no en-dear-ment worth ca-ress - ing, no ___ en-dear-ment, no en-

dear-ment worth ca-ress - ing.

DUET._"Come, ever-smiling liberty"

Soprano
Come, ev - er - smil - ing lib - er - ty, come,

Alto
Come, ev - er - smil - ing lib - er - ty,

smil - ing lib - er - ty, And with thee bring thy joc-und train,

smil - ing lib - er - ty, And with thee bring thy joc-und

and with thee bring thy joc - und train;

train, with thee bring thy joc - und train;

Come, ev - er - smil-ing lib-er -ty!

Come, ev - er - smil-ing lib-er - ty!

For thee we pant, and sigh for thee,——— and

For thee we pant, and sigh for thee, for thee we pant, and

20750

No 14. RECIT._ "My zealous father, now at rest"

JUDAS MACCABÆUS

My zeal-ous fa-ther, now at rest In the e-ter-nal man-sions of the blest: "Can ye be-hold," said he, "the mis-e-ries, In which the long-in-sult-ed Ju-dah lies? Can ye be-hold their dire dis-tress, And not, at least, at-tempt re-dress?" Then, faint-ly, with ex-pir-ing

breath: "Re-solve, my sons, on lib-er-ty, or death." We

come, we come! O see, thy sons pre-pare The rough ha-

bil-i-ments of war, With hearts in-trep-id, and re-venge-ful hands, To

ex-e-cute, O sire, thy dread com-mands.

attacca № 15

№ 15. TRIO AND CHORUS.—"Disdainful of danger"

dain-ful we'll rush on the foe,   That Thy pow'r, O Je -

dain-ful we'll rush on the foe,   That Thy pow'r, O Je -

dain-ful we'll rush on the foe,   That Thy pow'r, O Je -

ho-vah, all   na-tions may know, Thy pow'r, O Je - ho-vah,all   na-tions may

ho-vah, all   na-tions may know, Thy pow'r, O Je - ho-vah,all   na-tions may

ho-vah, all   na-tions may know, Thy pow'r, O Je - ho-vah,all   na-tions may

know.

know.

know.

con 8ve -

★ The parts in small type are additions. If they are sung, the notes in small type in the Chorus and Piano-forte parts must be considered.

64

20750

№ 16. RECIT._"Haste ye, my brethren"

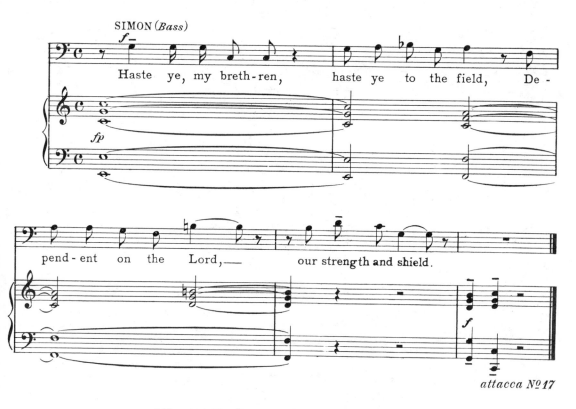

SIMON (*Bass*)

Haste ye, my breth-ren, haste ye to the field, De-pend-ent on the Lord,— our strength and shield.

attacca № 17

№ 17. CHORUS._"Hear us, O Lord"

Andante

Soprano — Hear us, O Lord, O Lord, on Thee we

Alto — Hear us, O Lord, O Lord, hear us, O Lord,

Tenor — Hear, hear us, O Lord, O Lord,

Bass — Hear,

Andante

67

20750

fall, re - solv'd on con - quest,

fall, re - solv'd on con - quest, re - solv'd

fall, re - solv'd on con - quest, re - solv'd, re - solv'd on

fall, re - solv'd on con - quest, re - solv'd on con - quest,

re - solv'd on con - quest, or glo - rious fall!

on con - quest, or a glo - rious fall!

con - quest, re - solv'd on con - quest! Hear us,

on con - quest, on con - quest, or a glo - rious fall!

74

20750

con - quest, or_____ a_ glo - - - rious fall, on con -

con - quest, or a glo - - rious, glo - - rious fall,

re - solv'd on

a_ glo - rious fall, a_ glo - rious fall, a glo - rious fall,

- quest, or a glo - rious fall, re - solv'd on

re - solv'd on con - quest, or glo - rious, glo - rious

con - quest, on con - quest,

re - solv'd on con - quest, or a glo - rious fall,

76

20750

O Lord, on Thee we call, Re-solv'd on con-quest, or a glo - rious

Thee, O Lord, on Thee we call, Re-solv'd on con-quest, or a glo - rious

Thee, O Lord, on Thee we call, Re-solv'd on con-quest, or a glo - rious

Thee, O Lord, on Thee we call, Re-solv'd on con-quest, or a glo - rious

fall!

fall!

fall!

fall!

Part II

№ 18. CHORUS.– "Fall'n is the foe"

Allegro moderato

80

CHORUS

Tenor: Fall'n is the foe, fall'n is the foe: so fall_ Thy foes, so

Bass: Fall'n is the foe, fall'n is the foe: so fall_ Thy foes, so

Soprano: Fall'n is the foe,

Alto: Fall'n is the foe:

fall Thy foes, oh Lord!

fall Thy foes, oh Lord!

so fall_ Thy foes;

Fall'n is the foe: so fall_ Thy foes,

-eous, right-eous sword, where war-like Ju - das wields____ his right - eous

wields____ his right - eous sword, his right - eous,

Where war - like Ju - das wields____ his right - eous,

sword, his right - eous sword, his right-eous sword.

where war - like Ju - das

right - - - eous sword, his right-eous sword, his right - eous

right - - - eous sword,

wields his right - - - - - eous

sword, where war-like Ju-das wields his right - - - eous

where war-like Ju - das wields___ his right - eous

cresc.

f   *mf*

B

Fall'n   is the foe,   where war-like Ju - das

sword.   Fall'n   is the foe,   where

sword.   Fall'n   is the foe:

sword.   Fall'n   is the foe: so

B

f

wields_____ his right - eous sword, his right - eous

war - like Ju - das wields his right - - -

so fall Thy foes, oh Lord, so

fall Thy foes, oh Lord!

sword. Fall'n is the foe, where

- - eous sword.

fall Thy foes, oh Lord! Where war - like Ju - das

Where war - like Ju - das wields his right - eous

war - like Ju - das wields his right-eous sword.

Fall'n is the foe, fall'n is the foe,

wields his right - eous sword.

sword. Fall'n is the foe,

Fall'n,

Fall'n,

Fall'n,

Fall'n,

fall'n, fall'n is the foe, fall'n,

fall'n, fall'n is the foe, fall'n,

fall'n, fall'n is the foe, fall'n,

fall'n, fall'n is the foe, fall'n,

fall'n is the foe, where war-like Ju - das wields his

fall'n is the foe,

fall'n is the foe,

fall'n is the foe,

88

20750

war - like Ju - das wields, wields,

war - like Ju - das wields, wields,

war - like Ju - das wields, wields,

war - like Ju - das wields, wields,

wields his right-eous sword.

wields his right-eous sword.

wields his right-eous sword.

wields his right-eous sword.

E

Fall'n, fall'n, fall'n is the foe: so

Fall'n, fall'n, fall'n is the foe: so

Fall'n, fall'n, fall'n is the foe: so

Fall'n, fall'n, fall'n is the foe: so

E

№ 19. DUET AND CHORUS.—"Sion now her head shall raise"

tune your harps to songs_____ of praise,

ISRAELITISH MAN (Tenor)

Si - on now her head__ shall raise, Tune your harps, tune your

harps, tune your harps to songs_____ of

Tune your harps to songs of__ praise,_____

praise,

94

20750

98

20750

№ 20. RECIT. "Oh, let eternal honours"

ISRAELITISH WOMAN (*Soprano*)

Oh, let e - ter - nal hon - ours crown his name, Ju-das! first Wor-thy in the rolls of fame. Say, "He put on the breast-plate as a gi-ant, and girt his war-like harness a - bout him; in his acts he was like a li-on, and like a li-on's whelp roar-ing for his prey."

attacca № 21

№ 21. AIR. "From mighty kings he took the spoil"

104

20750

might - y kings,— from might - y kings— he took the spoil,— And with his acts— made Ju - dah smile,— and with his— acts— made Ju - dah smile, smile,— smile,— Ah,— and with his acts,— and

with his acts___ made Ju - dah smile, ___ and with his acts made

Ju - dah smile, ___

cresc. _rit._

and with___ his acts_____ made

rit.

ossia:

Ju - dah smile.

a tempo

Nº 22. DUET (or Children's Choir) AND CHORUS
"Hail, Judea, happy land"

de - a!

hap - py land! Sal - va - - - - - - - - - tion

hap - py land! Sal - va - - - - - - tion pros -

hap - py land! Sal - va - - - - - - - tion

hap - py land! Sal - va - - - - - - - tion

Più largo

f a.2.

Sal - va - - - tion pros-pers in his hand.

pros - - - pers in his hand. _

- pers, pros - pers in his hand. _

pros - - - pers in his hand. _

pros - - - pers in his hand.

Più largo

Nº 23. RECIT._"Thanks to my brethren!"

JUDAS MACCABAEUS

mf
Thanks to my breth-ren! but, look up to Heav'n! To

p

Heav'n let glo-ry and all praise be giv'n: To Heav'n give your ap-

mp
plause, Nor add the sec-ond cause, As once your fa-thers did in Mid-ian,

mf

p

f
Say - ing, "The sword of God and Gid-eon." It was the Lord that

mf

mf

for His Is-rael fought, And this our won-der-ful sal-va-tion wrought.

Attacca Nº 2

Nọ 24. AIR.—"How vain is man"

vain_ is man, who boasts in fight

The val-our of gi - gan - - - - tic might,   the

val-our of gi - gan - - - - - - - - - - tic

might!   How vain_ is man, who boasts in fight,   wh

116

val - our of gi - gan - - - - - - - - - tic might!

How vain, how vain,— how vain— is man, who boasts— in fight,— who

boasts__ in fight The val-our of gi - gan - - tic might, the

val-our of gi - gan - - - - - - - -

(2da volta; rit.)

- - tic might, the val - - our of gi - gan-tic might!

Più tranquillo

And dreams not that a

Più tranquillo

Fine

118

hand un - seen Di - rects and guides this weak ma - chine,

and dreams not that a hand un - seen

di - rects and guides this weak ma - chine, di - rects and

guides, di - rects and guides this weak ma - chine. How

D. S.

No. **25.** RECIT. "Oh Judas, oh my brethren!"

Pto - le - my hath Mem-phis and Pe - lu-sium lost,) He sends the val - iant

Gor-gias,and commands His proud,vic-to-rious bands To root out Israel's strength,and to e -

rase Ev - 'ry me - mo - rial of the sa-cred place.

fp

mf

attacca Nº 26

No. 26. AIR AND CHORUS.— "Ah! wretched, wretched Israel!"

122

20750

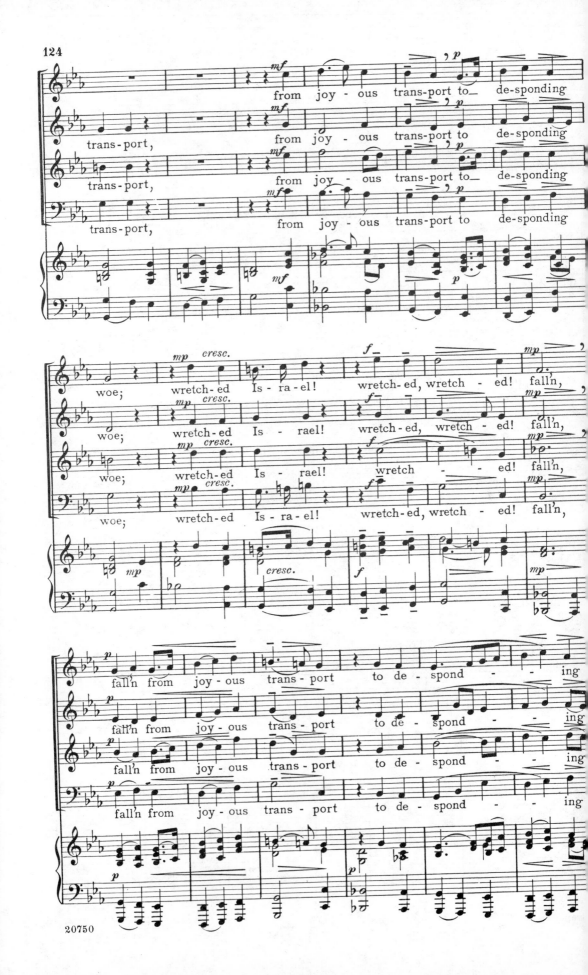

trans-port to de - spond - ing, de - spond - ing

trans-port to de - spond - ing, de - spond - ing

trans-port to de - spond - ing, de - spond - ing

trans-port to de - spond - ing, de - spond - ing

woe!

woe!

woe!

woe!

Tempo I

№ 27. RECIT.—"My arms!"

My arms! a - gainst this Gor-gias will I go! The
I - du - me - an gov - ern - or shall know How vain, how in - ef -
fect-ive his de-sign,While rage his lead-er, and Je - ho -vah mine.

No 28. AIR AND CHORUS.—"Sound an alarm!"

Sound an a - larm!___ your sil-ver trum-pets sound, your trum-pets sound, your trum-pets___ sound, And call the___ brave, and___ on-ly___brave, and call the___ brave, and___ on-ly___brave, and on - ly brave, a - round, call the brave, call the brave,___

and on - ly brave, a-

round!

Who list - eth, fol-low: to the field a - gain!

Jus-tice, with cour-age, is a ———— thou - sand — men, is a — thou-sand—

men, jus-tice, with cour-age, jus-tice, with cour-age, is a thou-sand— men, is a

thou-sand___ men, is a thou-sand men. Sound an a-larm!

Sound an a-larm, your sil-ver trumpets sound!___

And

call the___ brave, and___ on-ly___ your brave, and on-ly brave, a-

Nọ 29. RECIT._"Enough! To Heav'n we leave the rest"

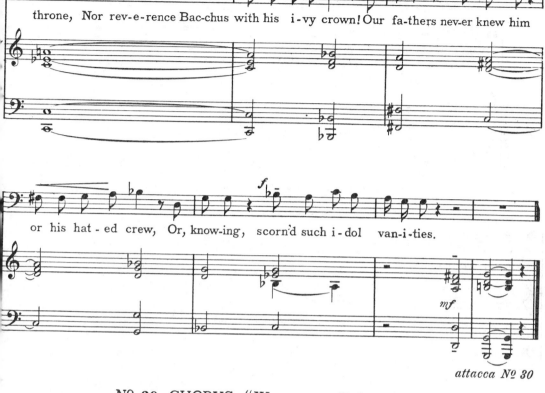

throne, Nor rev-e-rence Bac-chus with his i-vy crown! Our fa-thers nev-er knew him

or his hat-ed crew, Or, know-ing, scorn'd such i-dol van-i-ties.

attacca № 30

№ 30. CHORUS. "We never will bow down"

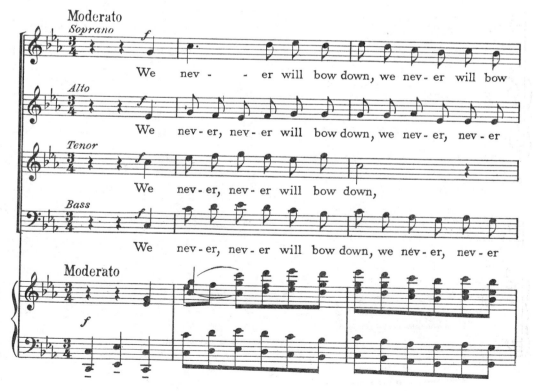

We nev - - er will bow down, we nev-er will bow

We nev-er, nev-er will bow down, we nev-er, nev-er

We nev-er, nev-er will bow down,

We nev-er, nev-er will bow down, we nev-er, nev-er

140

20750

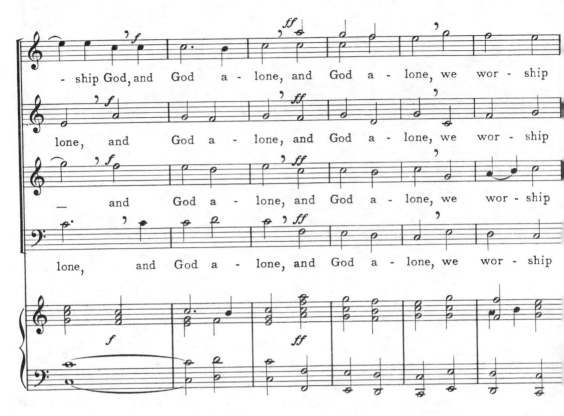

- ship God, and God a - lone, and God a - lone, we wor - ship

lone, and God a - lone, and God a - lone, we wor - ship

and God a - lone, and God a - lone, we wor - ship

lone, and God a - lone, and God a - lone, we wor - ship

God, and God a - lone, and God___ a - lone, we wor-ship God, we

God, and God a - lone, and God___ a - lone, we wor-ship

God, and God a - lone, and God___ a - lone,

God, and God a - lone, and God___ a - lone, we wor-ship

Part III

Nº **31**. AIR. − "Father of Heav'n!"

with ho - ly_ rites, To sol - em - nize_

_ the_ Feast of_ Lights, the_ Feast of_ Lights, to

sol - em - nize_____ the Feast of Lights, while we pre-pare, with

ho - - ly rites, to sol - em - nize_____ the Feast of Lights,

And thus our

grate - ful hearts em - ploy, And in Thy praise

This al-tar raise With car-ols of tri-umph-ant joy,— this al-tar—

raise with car-ols of tri - umph-ant joy,—

Ossia

— with car-ols of tri - umph - ant joy.— Fa-ther of Heav'n!

154

from Thy e-ter-nal throne, from Thy e-ter - nal throne

Look with an eye of bless-ing down, While we pre - pare,

__ with ho-ly rites, To sol-em-nize _____ the Feast of Lights, the Feast of

Lights, to sol-em-nize_____ the Feast of Lights.

№ 32. RECIT._"Oh grant it, Heav'n"

ISRAELITISH WOMAN (*Soprano*)

Oh grant it, Heav'n, that our long woes may cease, And Ju-dah's daugh-ters

taste the calm of peace; Sons, broth-ers, hus-bands to be-wail no

more, Tor-tur'd at home, or hav-ock'd in the war.

attacca № 33

№ 33. AIR._ "So shall the lute and harp awake"

shall the lute a-wake, so shall the harp a-wake, so shall the lute and harp a-wake, and spright-ly voice sweet des-cant run, and spright - ly voice sweet des - cant run, and spright - - - - - ly voice sweet des - cant run,___ and spright - - - - - -

158

20750

160

20750

-ly voice sweet des- cant run, __ se-raph- ic mel-o-

dy to make in the pure strains of Jes - se's son, se-raph - - -

- - - - - ic mel - o - dy to make in the pure strains

_ of Jes - - se's son.

_____ of Jes - se's son.

Nº 34. RECIT._"From Capharsalama on eagle wings I fly"

ISRAELITISH MESSENGER

From Ca - phar - sa - la - ma on ea - gle wings I fly, With ti - dings of im - pet - uous joy: Came Ly - si - as, with his host, ar - ray'd In coat of mail; their mas - sy shields Of gold and brass, flash'd light - ning o'er the fields; But Ju - das, un - dis - may'd, Met, fought, and van - quish'd all the rage - ful train.

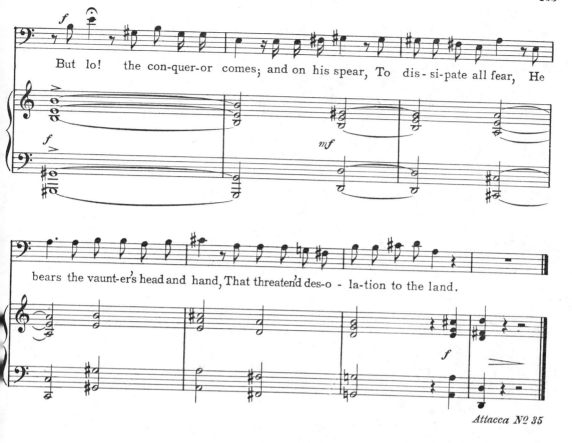

But lo! the con-quer-or comes; and on his spear, To dis-si-pate all fear, He

bears the vaunt-er's head and hand, That threaten'd des-o - la-tion to the land.

Attacca Nº 35

Nº 35. CHORUS.— "See, the conqu'ring hero comes!"

★ YOUTHS

Soprano I

See, the— con - qu'ring he - ro comes! Sound___ the

Soprano II

See, the— con - qu'ring he - ro comes! Sound___ the

Alto

See, the con - qu'ring he ro comes! Sound the

CHILDREN'S CHOIR

If a children's choir is not available, the part of *Youths* is sung by the ladies of the chorus, and the
art of *Virgins* by the Soloists (Soprano and Alto)

0750

trum-pets, beat the drums.

trum-pets, beat the drums.

trum-pets, beat the drums.

Sports pre - pare, the lau - rels

Sports pre - pare, the lau - rels

Sports pre - pare, the lau - rels

bring, Songs of tri - umph to him sing, Sports pre -

bring, Songs of tri - umph to him sing, Sports pre -

bring, Songs of tri - umph to him sing, Sports pre -

pare, the lau - rels bring, Songs___ of tri-umph to___ him sing.

pare, the lau - rels bring, Songs___ of tri-umph to___ him sing.

pare, the lau - rels bring, Songs of tri-umph to___ him sing.

VIRGINS

Sop. I.

See the___ god - like youth___ ad - vance! Breathe___ the

Sop. II.

See the___ god - like youth___ ad - vance! Breathe___ the

flutes, and lead___ the___ dance; Myr - tle-wreaths and

flutes, and lead___ the___ dance; Myr - tle-wreaths and

ros - es twine, To deck____ the he - ro's brow____ di -

ros - es twine, To deck____ the he - ro's brow____ di -

vine; Myr - tle - wreaths and ros - es twine, To

vine; Myr - tle - wreaths and ros - es twine, To

deck____ the he - ro's brow____ di - vine.

deck____ the he - ro's brow____ di - vine.

(With Children's Choir)

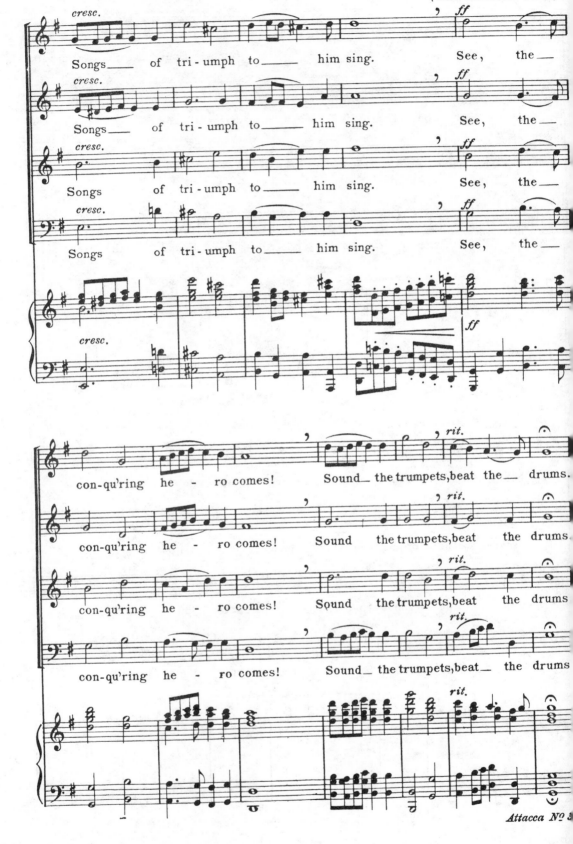

Songs___ of tri - umph to___ him sing. See, the___

Songs___ of tri - umph to___ him sing. See, the___

Songs of tri - umph to ___ him sing. See, the___

Songs of tri - umph to___ him sing. See, the___

con-qu'ring he - ro comes! Sound_ the trumpets, beat the _ drums.

con-qu'ring he - ro comes! Sound the trumpets, beat the drums.

con-qu'ring he - ro comes! Sound the trumpets, beat the drums

con-qu'ring he - ro comes! Sound_ the trumpets, beat_ the drums

Attacca N.° 3

№ 36. MARCH

Allegro

Attacca N?

Nº 37. CHORUS.—"Sing unto God"

Allegro maestoso

(Chorus) *Alto*

Sing un - to God, and high af - fec-tions raise, To crown this conquest with

* The three introductory measures in smaller type are an optional addition connecting the Chorus with the preceding March

un-mea - sur'd praise, _____ with un-

mea - sur'd praise. Sing un - to God, and high af-fec-tions raise, To

crown this con-quest with un-mea - sur'd praise, _____

A *Sop.*
Sing un - to God, and

Alto
Sing un - to God, and

Tenor
with un - mea - sur'd praise. Sing un - to God, and

Bass
Sing un - to God, and

A

to crown this con-quest with

crown this con-quest, to crown,_____ to crown this con-quest with un-

to crown, to crown, to crown___ this con-quest

un-mea - sur'd praise, to crown this con-quest with un-mea-sur'd,

un-mea - sur'd praise,_____

mea - sur'd praise, to crown, to crown, to crown___

with un - mea-sur'd praise, to crown___

with un-mea-sur'd praise, to crown, to crown, to

Optional version in small type

Nº 38. RECIT. – "Sweet flow the strains"

Nº 39. AIR. – "No unhallowed desire"

no,_____ Nor lust of un-bounded pow'r, nor lust of un-bound-ed

pow'r! No, no un-hal-low'd de-sire Our breasts shall in-spire, Nor

lust of un-bound-ed pow'r, nor lust of un-bound-ed pow'r,_____

nor lust of un-bound-ed

pow'r! But

peace to ob-tain,   Free peace let us gain,   And con-quest shall

ask no more,————   no more,   no more,   an

con-quest shall ask no more;

But peace t'ob-tain,   Free peace let us   gain,——   And con-quest shall ask no

more, and con-quest shall ask no more, no more, no

more, no more,

and conquest shall ask no more, But peace to ob-

tain, Free peace let us gain, And con-quest shall ask no

more!

Nọ 40. DUET._ "Oh lovely peace"

love-ly peace, with plen-ty crown'd, oh love-ly, love-ly peace! Come, spread

Poco più animato

Let the shrill trum-pet

Poco più animato

Let the shrill trum-pet cease, nor oth-er sound

But na-ture's

cease, nor oth-er sound

song - sters wake____ the cheer - ful morn, nor oth - er sound, nor

But na-ture's song - sters wake____ the

oth - er sound wake cheer - ful morn, but na - - ture's songsters wake the

cheer - ful morn, the cheer - ful morn, but na - - ture's songsters wake th

189

0750

love-ly peace, with plen-ty crown'd, oh love-ly, love-ly peace! Come, spread

thy_ bless-ings, thy_ bless-ings all_ a-round. Let

fleec-y flocks the hills a-dorn,_____ And val-leys smile wit

fleec-y flocks the hills a-dorn,_____ And val-leys smile wit

wav-y corn, let fleec-y flocks the hills a-dorn,

wav-y corn, and

Nº 41. AIR AND CHORUS.—"Rejoice, oh Judah!"

songs di - vine, with cher - u - bim and ser - a -phim har -

mo - nious join, and in songs___ di - vine har -

mo - nious join; re - joice, oh Ju-dah! re -

joice, oh Ju - dah! re - joice,_____ re -

Allegro, a tempo giusto
CHILDREN'S CHOIR ★

Hal - le - lu - jah, a - men,

Soprano

Alto

Hal - le - lu - jah, a - men,

Tenor

Hal - le - lu - jah, a - men,

Bass

Hal - le - lu - jah, a - men, a - men, hal - le - lu - jah, a - men.

Allegro, a tempo giusto

★ If a Children's choir is not available, the chorus sings the original version in small type
0750

re - joice,____ oh Ju - dah, in songs di -

re - joice, oh Ju - dah, in songs di -

re - joice,____ oh Ju - dah, in songs di -

re - joice,____ oh Ju - dah, in songs di -

CHILDREN (*Soprano*)

Hal - le - lu - -

vine, with cher - u - bim and ser - a - phim har - mo - - nious

vine, with cher - u - bim and ser - a - phim har - mo - - nious

vine, with cher - u-bim and ser - a-phim har - mo - - nious

vine,